WHO'S THERE?

by **Ann Fiore**

Illustrated by **John Steven Gurney**

A monkey is on the phone.

A zebra is on the phone.

A tiger is on the phone.

An ostrich is on the phone.

A giraffe is on the phone.

A snake is on the phone.

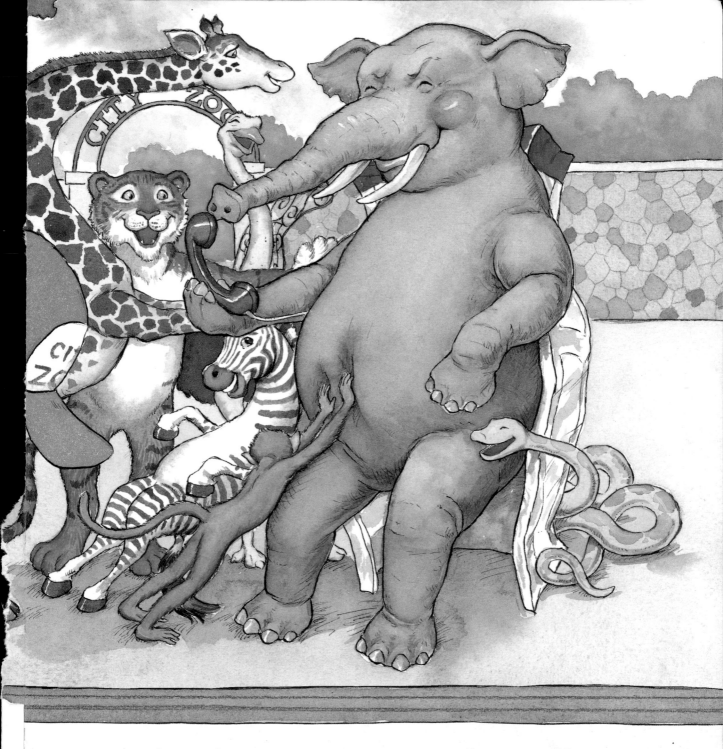

An elephant is on the phone.

CRUNCH!
An elephant is
on the phone.